To the Reader:

This unique book offers you the exact safe and supportive words to use when telling a 3-5 year old child a loved one has died. *Honey Bear Died* maintains the language and repetition that a preschooler demands while also using terms specific for this age and developmental comprehension to eliminate any confusion, misconceptions or fears.

Honey Bear Died is written so you can explain what dead means by simply reading the entire story word-for-word without having to adjust or modify it. It also uses a unique concept of having words in red which you can change to fit the child's situation. The end result is you safely and supportively telling the child in an understandable way that someone has died.

Honey Bear Died is exclusive in providing for this overlooked age group by being the first to introduce this concept in simple, concrete ways to support 3-5 year olds.

About *Honey Bear Died*:

The idea of having to introduce a child to the concept of death easily brings tears to an adult's eyes. This is a sensitive subject that adults typically request assistance with. In my many years of working with children and families in grief I have become increasingly aware of the gap in resources for children ages 3-5. Often adults ask "What words do I use?" and "How do I tell my child, they are so young?" As a result, *Honey Bear Died* was created.

The unique style of *Honey Bear Died* eliminates the adult's worry about saying the wrong thing or not knowing what to say. *Honey Bear Died* offers this assistance and support by being exactly what the adults need from a book and the words 3-5 year old children need to hear. *Honey Bear Died* is a must-have for families and those who support families in the grieving process. *Honey Bear Died* is a necessity for any parent, caregiver, teacher, funeral director, counselor, therapist, librarian, church, grief support center and simply anyone who has children in their life, personally or professionally.

Honey Bear Died

Written By Jennifer E. Melvin
Illustrated by Kerry DeBay

Honey Bear Died

Limitless Press, LLC
Distributed by Lightning Source, a subsidary of Ingram

ISBN 978-1-61335-052-2
Updated Edition - 2021

This publication is designed to provide information in regard to
the subject matter covered. It is sold with the understanding that
the publisher is not engaged in rendering psychological services.
If expert assistance or counseling is needed, the services of a
qualified professional should be sought.

To order more copies of this book please visit:
www.limitlesspress.com
or email: sales@limitlesspress.com
Quantity discounts available for non-profit
and educational organizations.

Opportunity to Personalize:

Honey Bear Died provides the unique opportunity to personalize the story in a simple, easy to use manner. For example, a young child's grandma called "Meemaw" died. Notice the change of the words in red to the underlined words to fit the child's experience.

I have some sad news to tell you.
~~Grandpa Honey Bear~~ <u>Meemaw</u> died.
This is sad because it means we won't be able to see ~~Honey Bear~~ <u>Meemaw</u> anymore.
We won't be able to play with ~~Honey Bear~~ <u>Meemaw</u> anymore either.
We won't be able to see ~~him~~ <u>her</u> or do any fun things with ~~him~~ <u>her</u> anymore because ~~he~~ <u>she</u> died.

The words are written in red to identify those that can be altered; however, it is important to note they all don't have to be. Notice that the "we" in the third, fourth and fifth sentences was fitting for this child and not changed. By modifying the words in red text, you can fit the story to the child while feeling confident you are maintaining the proper terminology. Also note this is created as an opportunity to personalize the reading, but not a necessity. By reading the book as is, the child receives all of the necessary and age-appropriate words to explain what it means when someone we love dies.

I have some sad news to tell you.
Grandpa Honey Bear **died.**

This is sad because it means we **won't be able to see** Honey Bear **anymore.** We **won't be able to play with** Honey Bear **anymore either.** We **won't be able to see** him **or do any fun things with** him **anymore because** he **died.**

When someone dies their body stops working.
They can't hear.   They can't smell.

They can't see. They can't talk.

Their heart doesn't beat because their body doesn't work anymore.

They can't do any of the things we can do because we are alive. When we are alive our body works. We can see: "Peek a boo"

We can smell: "What do you smell now?"
We can hear: "Do you hear me say your name?"

We can talk: "Say my name"
Our heart beats and helps our body work.
Put your hand on your heart, it goes budump budump.

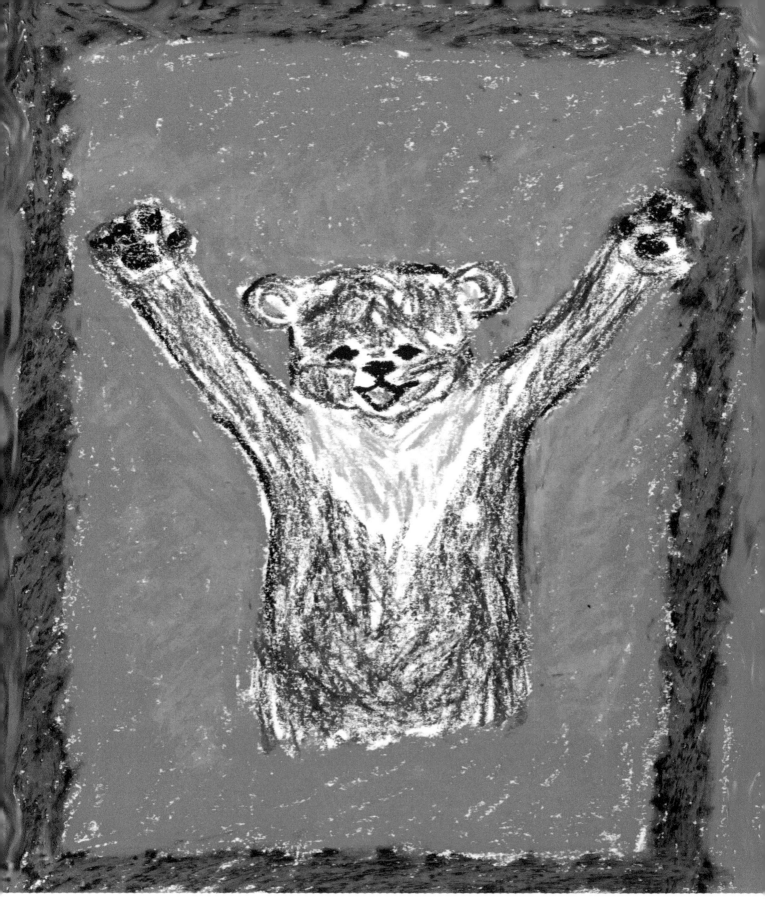

We can do all of these things because our body works and we are alive.

**It's ok to miss Grandpa Honey Bear being alive.
It makes me really sad that Honey Bear died.**

I am going to miss playing with him. I am also going to miss seeing him and doing fun things with him because he died. I know you will too.

When we miss someone we can feel really sad. It's ok to feel sad because Honey Bear died. Can I you give you a big bear hug to make you feel a little better?

Common grief responses of children ages 3 – 5
- Think that what happened might only be temporary (ex. Death is reversible)
- Temper tantrums
- Regressive behaviors (thumb sucking, bed wetting)
- Clinginess
- Crying
- Repeated questions
- Nightmares
- May grieve, then play, then grieve, then play- or only play and not appear to be sad
- May bring out blankets, toys, etc. that they used to play with or use
- Somatic complaints (headaches, stomach aches, etc.)

Children this age will continue to believe what happened is temporary due to their developmental level of understanding death. This is normal and as they advance developmentally they will discover permanence in death between ages 6 and 9. The other responses listed above may last for a bit of time but should gradually fade when the tips of How to help a grieving 3-5 year old are consistently used.

Tips: How to help a grieving 3-5 year old
- Give simple, repeated explanations
- State the truth with age appropriate information and/or "I don't know"
- Use words such as *dead* and *died*- Death means the body no longer works
- Provide a secure, loving environment and nurturing assurances
- Provide physical comforting
- Actively (attentively) listen, acknowledge their feelings & what happened
- Draw, read books and play together, allowing them to release their emotions in safe ways
- Maintain structure and routine
- Use the word "choice" or "choose" when asking them what they want to do, eat, etc. Ex. "What do you choose?" (Highlighting that they have choices and using the word helps create a sense of control)

Tips: What NOT to do
- Don't let your sense of helplessness keep you from reaching out
- Don't avoid the child because you feel uncomfortable
- Don't use words such as lost, sleeping, passed away to describe death or the person who died **these can create fears- use proper words "dead" , "died"
- Don't change the subject when they mention the person who died
- Don't always try to fix it

How to know when to ask for help
- When you feel you or your child needs it
- When the change you are seeing in your child lasts for an extended period of time and/or the change has intensified to a concerning level
- If any changes impact the child's health, physical or emotional well being
- When you feel you or your child could benefit from it

Author **Jennifer E. Melvin** is a Licensed Clinical Social Worker, Certified Bereavement Facilitator, Certified Trauma and Loss Specialist and a trained professional in death, dying and bereavement with a Certification in Thanatology. Jennifer has a background in mental health, chronic/terminal illness and life transitions with years of experience specializing in clinical and supportive grief & loss services for children, teens and families.

Illustrator **Kerry DeBay** is a Board-Certified, Registered Art Therapist, Licensed Mental Health Counselor, Certified Trauma Specialist, Registered Yoga Teacher and author of *The Grief Bubble: Helping Kids Explore and Understand Grief*. She has over 20 years of professional experience working with children and adults as a clinician and trainer/educator. Kerry's extensive experience working with grief and loss inspired and guided her in authoring *The Grief Bubble* and illustrating *Honey Bear Died*.

Lightning Source UK Ltd.
Milton Keynes UK
UKHW051130180123
415542UK00008B/114